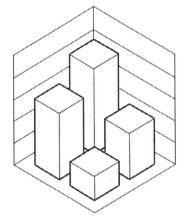

Data Handling
in Primary Science

Doug Dickinson
& Tina Jarvis

Published by SCIcentre

School of Education, University of Leicester, 21 University Road, Leicester LE1 7RF

© SCIcentre 2001

ISBN: 1 902 126 130

SCIcentre was established in 1996 with Homerton College Cambridge and the Society of Chemical Industry.

Designed by AVS Graphics and printed by AVS Print at the University of Leicester.

Acknowledgements

The illustrative examples have been taken from:

Research Machines PLC: RM Starting Graph and RM Number Magic

Granada Learning / Black Cat: First Workshop, Information Workshop and Number Magic

Softease: Textease

Contents

What is
Data Handling?

Introduction

Making sense of all of the information around us is an essential skill in this data rich society. The data comes to us in many different forms: text, graphics, charts, tables, sound and video animation. To ensure that our children can cope with this wealth of information, we must teach them how to decode, sort and sift, reject and accept and, of course, interpret. We must also teach them how to compile information, taking account of the audience for whom it is intended.

Developing all of these abilities requires time, skill and resources.

Handling information or data handling, particularly in an educational context, usually begins with a question that needs an answer, e.g. do people walk to school because they think that it is healthy? Is plastic the best 'waterproofer'? Do all plants, given the same conditions, grow at the same rate? Once the question(s) has been asked it is possible to determine what data needs to be collected to provide the answers. Consequently, data handling involves collecting together all sorts of information, arranging it and rearranging it to look for patterns, similarities and differences so that we can answer a question or to prompt us to look for other questions.

Databases are the tools which allow us to manipulate the data and look for correlations. They give opportunities to store, sort and display information in lots of different ways. Before the advent of electronic ways of doing this, man's ingenuity devised many paper ways of sorting vast amounts of information and companies made fortunes based on their card-file indexes. If there are only a few pieces of information to look at, it is probably still better to use a pencil and some paper to store the details. Electronic databases come into their own when a lot of information is to be collected and when time and human error might become factors in a manual system.

Science frequently involves posing and answering questions. Therefore, scientists need to be able to use database programs to handle the data that they collect. They use their skills, as scientists, to collect, organise and analyse this data. This helps them to see relationships between different factors which prompt new questions. They can then test out their ideas and pose further questions. It also enables them to compare their interpretations with those of other people working in the same field.

How do we begin to **make sense of data?**

From the Womb to the World

Even before you are born your senses are being bombarded with data which is processed automatically by your body. Fantastic isn't it ! From the moment you are born every bit of you begins to pick up information about the World around you. Your ears begin to sense sounds, your eyes detect changes in light and you touch variations in texture. Each of your senses begins to build files in your personal database, your brain. The data gathering at this stage is open-ended. There is no attempt to collate it. The multi-sensory experiences give rise to generic questions which are answered by a variety of means, often by experimentation and interpretation of the results. 'Is the table good to eat?' would be an example.

All this information needs to be grouped or it would be overwhelming. A toddler points to a black cat... 'Cat', says the closest adult. A black thing on 4 legs goes by... 'Cat,' says the toddler's brain. But no, the second one was a dog. 'Dog,' says the adult. Lots of information to be processed here... what makes a cat a cat and what makes a dog a dog. More information and experience is needed. This information is gradually collated – Smoky, grey, long whippy tail, scratches, meows... cat; Tom, black, long whippy tail, scratches, meows... cat; Rusty, black, short stumpy tail, barks... dog; and so on. This develops into a database of 4 legged furry/hairy animals. There is no attempt to represent the data. None is needed.

And so it goes on. Adults, friends, teachers, helpers, enemies, books, TV, computers, video, tapes, radio and 'real' experiences all go together to build up the database. Sometimes different bits of data appear to conflict. So time, help and experience are needed to make sense of it. Making sense of it is the tricky bit.

Starting School

This procedure continues when a child first goes to school. Initially, the data about school is unsorted, but very soon these multi-sensory experiences give rise to generic questions.... 'What are lessons?' ... 'Is playtime always after milk?' ... 'Why am I in the red group when I like yellow best?'

Questions keep on being asked and patterns of answers begin to form. It is all about looking for patterns. When the patterns are known then they can begin to be used to amend and make sense of other experiences.

In time the patterns need to be recorded so that they are not forgotten.....PE kit day, homework timetables, money for school trip etc. These are recorded in a way which makes sense to the recorder and are not intended to be communicated and shared. When the data needs to be shared then conventions take over so that the sharing is efficient. After all, it would not do if bank accounts were constructed so that the bank and the customer worked in different units!

Recording and Sharing Data

Collection of data always begins in an open-ended way. This open look at things is a huge strength and provokes the collector to look for patterns in the information. This looking leads to the creation of hypotheses, which, when tested, leads to the asking of further questions.

Early on in the process, if little data is available then the collection is by sensing and committing to memory. Its representation is 'virtual' and/or its communication is by mouth (answering questions or giving information). For example, one child might look to see how many birds are eating at the bird table.

In order to clarify the information and to share it, we need to find ways of representing it and communicating it to others. The information about the birds on the bird table could be represented manually in a tally chart or table. The data could then be viewed and interpreted by anyone who wants to know. This will work well if the data sample is still small.

However, the data may need to be collected over a long period of time. For example, to answer the question *How many birds eat at the bird table between 10 am and 11 am each day and is this different each month of the year?* the data needs to be collected in a way in which many people can contribute. It then needs to be represented so that they can all see the answer to the question. This is where an electronic database comes into its own. The more data that needs collecting, the more it becomes necessary to employ electronic means for efficient and effective collation.

Knowing when and how to use an
Electronic Database

It is important to start to help children understand how to collect, manipulate, record and communicate data by sorting and recording data manually and on paper before electronic databases are introduced.

There are two main stages in making sense of data:

- The exploration of data in an open way to generate questions
- Using and refining the data to answer and communicate the answers to specific questions

There is also a variety of 'sorting' or 'data handling' approaches including:

- card files
- branching databases
- flat files
- spreadsheets

Each of these approaches should be 'done' manually, on paper, as well as electronically. The children need to be introduced to each approach and to their uses throughout the primary school so that by the top of the primary school the children know the differences between them and how each may be used.

The process of using data handling to raise and answer questions

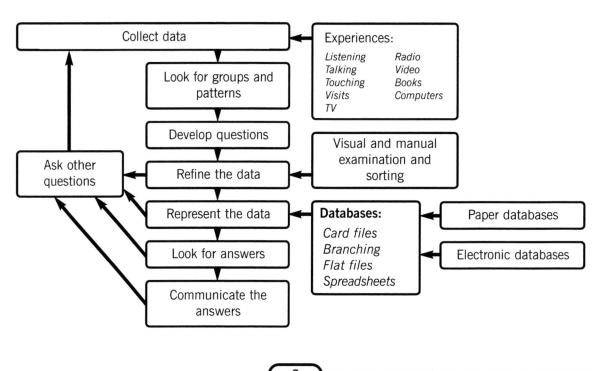

Practical and Paper Methods First

Initially the children need to be introduced to any new technique very practically. It is important that children see how and why a method of representing data is appropriate before an electronic database is introduced.

Developing Children's Independence in the use of Electronic Databases

Initially the electronic version should be demonstrated by the teacher so that it will be understood by the children. Over time the teacher should enable the children to have a greater independence in choosing and manipulating their chosen data handling application.

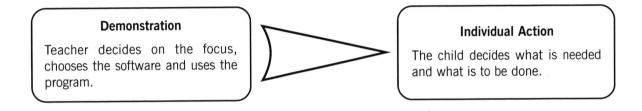

Demonstration
Teacher decides on the focus, chooses the software and uses the program.

Individual Action
The child decides what is needed and what is to be done.

At first the teacher provides considerable guidance and support followed by a staged transfer of responsibility to the children.

▶ **Stage 1: Whole class teacher demonstration**

The teacher should model the activity for the children by demonstrating and explaining the use of the computer, explaining the software and the process of loading the software. The teacher might sit with keyboard on his/her knee with the monitor at the side as an electronic blackboard. The process here is one of demonstration. If more advanced tools of ICT are available such as interactive whiteboard, data projector or even a large monitor, so much the better. This is quite a long stage and should not be shortcut. Before the children use a piece of software on their own they need to have seen it in use for a similar purpose to their project as often as possible.

▶ **Stage 2: Teacher assisted by the whole class**

Once the children are relatively familiar with the software and approach, the teacher continues to use the computer as a blackboard but invites the children to contribute by 'clicking' or typing etc.

▶ **Stage 3: Supported groupwork led by the teacher**

Here the teacher plans the lesson to allow for him/her to sit with a group of 6 – 8 children to support their work with the computer and to discuss specific curriculum and ICT information.

▶ **Stage 4: Groupwork supported by the teacher**

At this stage the teacher withdraws from the group and only visits the group to keep the pace going or to answer specific questions. The rate of withdrawal of support will depend upon the skill and techniques available to the group. Observant teachers will ensure that the group dynamics legislates for total involvement. The children's activity should be a known and practised one so that success can be optimised.

▶ **Stage 5: Paired work giving more autonomy for each child**

The progression moves on to more independent work. The activity should again be a known one so that confidence and competence continue to be built up.

▶ **Stage 6: Individual and integrated activities**

The process of moving towards autonomous use of ICT to support learning is secured at the moment the child suggests its use to perform a particular task and can use the type of database selected reasonably and effectively to answer the question in hand.

A check list is provided in the appendix to help teachers monitor each child's developing independence (page 58).

Introducing different types of database

The progression from teacher modelling to children's independence will need to be developed for each type of database, with the speed of progression depending on the children's personal understanding and ICT capability.

Children should be doing very simple data handling activities in the Foundation Stage (ages 4 – 6). These early activities will provide a secure basis for introducing the three main types of databases that will be used in the primary school, namely:

- Flat files
- Branching
- Spreadsheets

Planning for progression

Each school should plan when each type of database will be first introduced to the children so that they satisfy the requirements of the Numeracy Strategy as well as the ICT National Curriculum. The diagram on page 12 gives one such plan. It also shows some of the science topics that can give the context for their use. These particular topics have been chosen so that they match with the Science QCA Scheme of work for Key Stages 1 & 2.

Whether a computer is going to be used or not, information handling requires much thought and planning before starting. The following questions can help to clarify the approach needed:

- Why is the information going to be gathered? Is there a question to be answered?
- What information will be needed?
- How will the information be collected?
- Where will the information come from?
- How will the information be organised?
- Which ICT tool will be best for the job, if at all?

Introducing different graphical representations

The results of data collection and analysis are often presented in the form of graphs. There are many ways in which data can be displayed graphically:

- Venn and Carroll diagrams
- Pictograms
- Block charts and histograms
- Pie charts
- Line graphs

Each has its own purpose. These also need to be introduced progressively alongside the different databases, again with the teacher demonstrating when, how and why each form should be used. This should be done in a way that enables the children to make their own decisions about what to use and to be independent in their application.

A **Progression** for **Developing Data Handling**

The columns show when different types of databases and different graph types might be introduced in the primary school. Each of these topics is covered in detail in the next part of the book. Whenever any new database or graphical representation is introduced, children should start with 'real' data before being given support to enable them to work independently on computer.

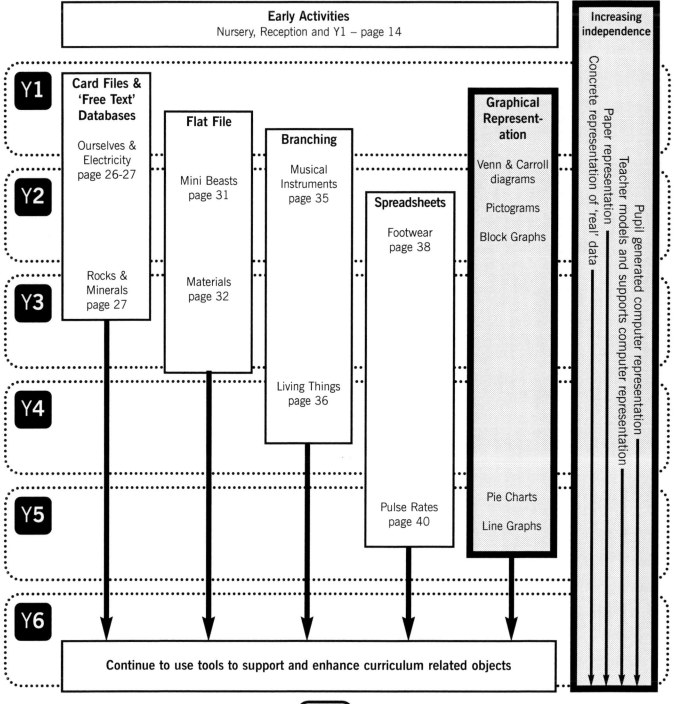

Working Towards
Independence

A Case Study: **Developing independent data handling** in a **Year 1** class

This case study shows how a teacher developed a progression in information handling skills with his Year 1 class in a very practical way. It demonstrates how the ICT component was introduced alongside the more manual ways of handling information.

Ourselves Topic: We are all different

The project, which focused on human similarities and differences, took place over one school term.

▶ **Session 1: Observing differences in the class to introduce sorting in a practical way**

- Time: 5/10mins circle time
- Style: Teacher led
- Resources: Mr Men books, the children & cards for writing down hair colour.

This activity was introduced as part of a series of story sessions based on the 'Mr Men' books. The teacher read one of the stories and then said...

> *These Mr Men are all different they have different habits and do different things... A bit like you really.*

> *Just look at your friends in the class. They are all children but they are all different in many ways. Can you tell me any differences?*

Then followed a free and frank discussion about differences. The teacher finally focused attention on hair colour.

> *Fine, so let's think about the differences in the colour of hair we see.*
> *Who thinks that they have fair hair?*
> *Who thinks that their hair is dark?*
> *Who thinks that their hair is red?*
> *And who thinks that their hair is brown?*

> *Have a good look at your friend's hair and between you decide what colour it is. Now get your friend to look at yours. Try to decide whether it is fair, dark, red or brown. Just one of these.*

> *Now let's sort the class. If you think your hair is fair, go and stand over there. One of you hold this label with 'fair' on it. If it is dark, stand over there. If it is red, go over there and if it is brown, go over there.*

When all of the children had sorted themselves out into the 4 corners of the room the teacher said,

> *Have a good look at your group. Do you all agree about the hair colour?*

The teacher discreetly moved anyone who was obviously out of place saying,

> *That looks about right... We have sorted you into groups according to the colour of your hair.*

▶ **Session 2: Introducing a paper representation of the sorted data**

- Time: 15mins
- Style: Teacher led
- Resources: the children, cards with the hair colour on & cards with body shapes.

The teacher asked the children if they could remember how they had sorted everyone into groups according to their hair colour. He commented that he could not remember how many of the class had dark hair and said that he wished that he had kept a record.

> *I hope you can remember what colour you said your hair was.*

> *I have made some body cards here. Just colour the hair in either fair, dark, red or brown and then put your name on the bottom and let me have your card.*

> *Now let's sort the cards. Each card is a little picture of you. It represents you and your hair colour. Here are all the fair ones. Here are all the dark ones. Here are the red ones so that makes these the brown ones.*

> *Let's check this data about your hair colour. There should be ** children in this class with fair hair.*

The teacher counted the cards out loud with the children.

> *Would all of those children who coloured the hair fair on their body cards go and stand over there.*

The teacher matched the number to the card and the activity was repeated for the other colours. This was the moment when a representation of the data (hair colour) was used instead of the actual objects. The body cards were then stuck on a notice board inside circles to represent the data collected.

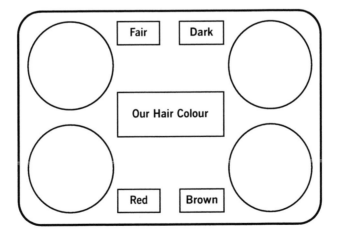

As the representation was a 'body' picture, the children were able to see the relationship of the real data (themselves) to the drawn format. The next step was to use less obvious things to represent each characteristic but to ensure that the children were still clear about the link between the real phenomenon and the representation.

▶ **Session 3: Revisiting the sorting activity in a new context and the introduction of more 'abstract' representations**

- Time: 20 mins
- Style: Teacher led
- Resources: 'Mr Men' books, the children, cards for writing down the eye colour, plastic mirrors, cubes & 'eye pictures'.

Again the teacher used the 'Mr Men' books to prompt the children to look for differences saying:

> *There are lots of differences in these 'Mr Men'... just look and think of some of them. There are lots of things different about you too.*

> *Today we are going to look at the colour of your eyes because when we were talking about this last time lots of you noticed that people have different coloured eyes.*

Teacher gave out plastic mirrors and the children looked at their eyes.

> *Let your friend help you to decide what your eye colour is. When you have sorted it out, find the cube that is the closest match to that colour. Then take a picture of an eye and carefully colour it in.*

> *You should now have a cube and a picture (coloured in). Now let's look and see what eye colours we have so that we can start to sort them out.*

The teacher used the card to make a label for each eye colour as he had done in the previous activity for hair colour. He then helped the children to sort themselves into groups with one child in each group holding the 'eye colour' card. This was easier than before with the hair colours as the children knew what to expect having done a similar activity. Once this was done the teacher said:

> *Everyone in your group should have the same colour eyes and should have the same colour cube and should have coloured their eye picture in in the same way.*

> *We can use the pictures and the cubes to show or represent the data we have collected.*

The teacher asked one of the children from each group to make a tower of the cubes and asked the others to notice what was happening.

> *The tower of cubes represents the number of children in the group with ** coloured eyes.*

The pictures of the eyes were then stuck onto a chart similar to the one used for hair colour.

Now the children had been shown three ways of representing data:

- themselves in groups
- sets of coloured eye pictures
- towers of cubes which matched the eye colours

The teacher pointed out that even when they went to sit back down on their chairs, the information about the colour of their eyes could still be seen.

▶ **Session 4: Using an electronic method to represent the data**

- Time: 5/10mins circle time

- Style: Teacher led

- Resources: the children & a computer.

The children were reminded of the previous 'hair' and 'eye' activities by referring them to the data representations around the room. Then the teacher said:

We are all different aren't we? We have looked at the colour of our hair and the colour of our eyes... you know we have not looked at the most obvious difference yet... some of us are boys and some are girls!

All the girls just move to this side of the room. Now all the boys just shuffle to that side. There you are... sorted.

You boys take a blue cube and girls, you take a red one. Now quickly and quietly build the tower to represent your group.

The teacher took the towers and stood them up, counted the cubes in each, checking the data.

This activity revised the previous sessions. The teacher wished to show that the data could be collected quickly and simply (sitting on the carpet) and it could be represented just as quickly.

We can represent this data in a simple way on our computer.

The teacher loaded up a graphing package and explained that he was going to represent the data that they had collected on the computer. He asked the children to count the number of girls and then the number of boys. He checked it again by counting the cubes. The teacher then put the headings on the columns for the data collection and the children came forward and 'clicked' with the mouse to enter their information.

As they did this the teacher said:

This picture on the screen is showing the data we have collected... We can save it and print it out. It shows the same data as the cubes. What data is that?

The teacher asked the children to make the link between the real phenomena (themselves), the tower of cubes and the pictorial representation. It is important to reinforce the concept that the method of display does not affect the data.

The teacher showed the children how to put a title on the graph, save it and print it out. The children were finally asked to draw pictures of themselves to put into a hooped Venn diagram. The cubes were arranged alongside (threaded and hung up with a suitable label) next to the Venn diagram. The computer generated block graph was printed out and placed near the other two.

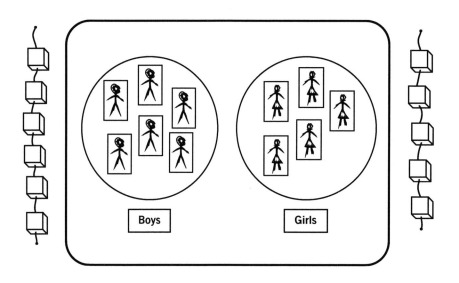

▶ Session 5: Representing the range

- Time: 30 mins
- Style: Teacher led
- Resources: the children, string, cubes, card labels, items that could be used to represent height & a computer

The teacher continued the theme of differences by investigating height. He said:

We are all different aren't we. When we were talking about this last time you noticed lots of differences. Today I want to have a look at a really obvious one. Stand up!! It is quite clear that even though you are all 6 years old you are not all the same height.

Let's see if we can line you all up... smallest at that end and the tallest at this...

Well, you can really see that this is another of the big differences. If we look at the person at each end and stand them back to back we can just see how big this difference is over the whole class. This is called the range.

We could represent this data that we have collected by drawing round everyone and then putting the shapes up on the wall but that would take an awful lot of space. I wonder how else we could do it.

The teacher hoped that someone would make the connection with cubes or other artefacts. Someone suggested wool or string and another did say cubes. The teacher pointed out tactfully that cubes weren't a good idea because they would take far too many and that string might be a good idea... (He had a ball of string handy and visible).

The children also mentioned that the data could be shown on the computer. In this case the teacher needed a way of quantifying the information as a number. The teacher guided the children to think how they could measure their height. There was much discussion about an appropriate method. The children suggested using large blocks, footsteps and ruler lengths etc. They settled for using one of the big wooden blocks as the 'unit' for measurement.

The children were then set to representing their heights with lengths of string and attaching labels to the bottom of each piece. They wrote their names and how many blocks tall they were on the label. These representations were then displayed. They were hung from a common point so that they could be directly compared.

In plenary mode, the teacher then suggested that the data could have been represented on the computer. With keyboard on knee and the children watching, the teacher opened an appropriate graphing program and entered each child's data based on their measurements using the big wooden blocks.

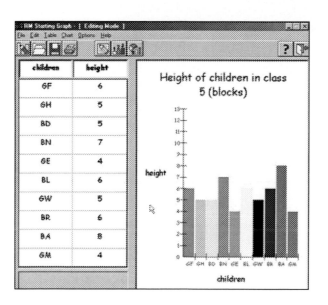

The teacher again emphasised that the data on the computer screen was the same as the data they had collected and represented physically with the strings. He checked the information and, showing the children again how to save and print, pinned the printout next to the strings to show that data can be represented in a variety of forms.

▶ Session 6: Supported group work using the computer

- Time: 30 mins
- Style: Teacher support
- Resources: the children & a computer

The teacher prompted the children to think up some 'new' differences:

We are all different aren't we?

We have already looked at hair colour, eye colour, gender (that's whether you are a boy or a girl) and height. What other differences did we notice?

Let's make a list.

The list included shoe size, hand size, weight, colour of jumper, colour of shoes, favourite foods, pets and other 'favourites', whether they walked to school or not, whether they could swim or not etc. The teacher wrote all of the 'differences' on cards, deliberately avoiding 'weight' as this can be stressful for some children, and shuffled them. He then said:

Now, as part of our work for a while we are going to collect data about all of these differences. I am going to work with one group to collect the data about one 'difference' whilst the rest of you get on with the other work I have set. You will all get a turn so don't worry.

The teacher settled with the first group. The cards with the 'differences' on were placed face down on the table and one was chosen. If the group didn't like it they were allowed to return it to the table and select another one. They were only allowed to do this once. When the 'difference' had been selected the teacher supported the group through the process of collecting and then representing the data on the computer which already had the graphing package on it loaded and open.

The teacher supported the children in collecting, entering and saving the data. He also guided them through the printing process.

▶ **Session 7: A recap on styles of representation to show how data can be stored on paper and electronically**

- Time: 30 mins
- Style: Teacher led – plenary
- Resources: the children, string, large paper & a computer

The teacher talked about some of the differences which had been investigated and invited each of the groups to come out and explain the data they had collected and saved as files on the computer. He talked about the way that the computer saved the data so that they could view it again and again. He also said that if there were any changes to the data it would be easy to make them using the program on the computer.

He asked the group who had looked at 'birthdays' to demonstrate this because he knew that there had been 2 birthdays in the class since the data had been entered. Members of the 'birthday' group organised the class into age groups and checked their data. They made the appropriate alterations and saved and reprinted the information.

The teacher commented that when collecting data it was always a good idea to date it so that it could be said that it was 'correct on such and such a date'.

This showed that information stored electronically can be quickly recovered for further investigation.

Further Early Activities

All of the sorting activities common in early years classes are useful in adding to the range of experience of sorting and classifying real objects and in looking for similarities and differences. Many of these can be started in a practical way, then recorded using paper and electronic means along the lines of the previous detailed case study.

Teddies

For example, a very similar sequence can be done using the children's own teddies. A lesson where the children bring in their own teddy bears can lead to activities which sort the teddies by colour, standing or sitting, old or young etc. The ideas can be extended by balancing the teddies with conkers or bobbins to say which weighs the most or by lining up cubes next to them to represent heights.

Weather

The daily recording of the weather by cutting out and sticking pictures into a table or a chart on a notice board is an important Key Stage 1 activity. This can also be paralleled with a similar activity on the computer. The computer based activity is a way of showing the children how information can be collected and displayed quickly and simply. The recording can be done on a daily basis.

This can be collated on a frequency chart as shown bottom right. Weather icons drawn by the teacher or children can be cut out and stuck on. Later this can be done electronically with various preprepared packages.

Daily Record

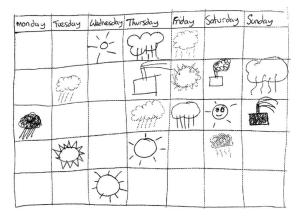

Frequency Chart

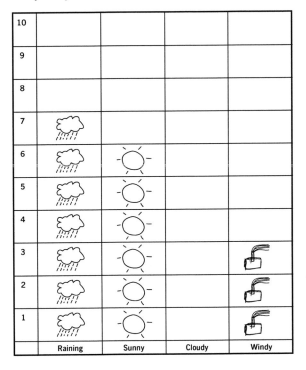

Sorting for buoyancy, magnetism and conductivity

Early years children are introduced to the language 'float' and 'sink' by practically testing a variety of items such as cork, stones, paper clips, plastic balls etc. The teacher can encourage the children to explore the items over several sessions. The initial record might include putting the items in two labelled hoops. Once the children have understood the task, the teacher can suggest that a more permanent record would be useful with the children making a drawing of each item in a simple Venn diagram. The final stage is to use the computer to produce the drawing of the Venn diagram.

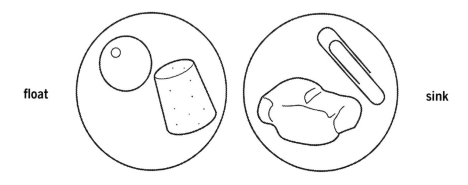

float   sink

The same process can also be adopted when sorting magnetic and non-magnetic items, as well as things that conduct and do not conduct electricity.

When the children are familiar with the science concepts, they can be revised to consider two properties in a Carroll diagram.

	Float	Sink
Magnetic		✂
Non Magnetic		

It can be seen that common early years activities can be extended in a manageable way that introduces children to electronic databases so that the children can see the relationship between their practical experiences and the computer generated images.

Introducing Different
Databases

Card Files and 'Free Text' Databases

Card files or 'Free Text' files are fairly simple so are suitable for very young children, as well as having a wide range of applicability.

Punch Cards

In the days before electronic databases much information was kept on punch cards. Information was carried on the cards by having a hole or a slot. The process of interrogating the information was done by pushing a rod through the holes and then extracting those cards which stayed on the rod. These were the ones which exhibited the property required.

Making real punch cards with young children can provide a helpful way to show them how a 'free text' database in a computer works.

Names

Each child can be given a piece of card with a hole punched in it and one corner cut off. They write their first names on the card and draw a picture of themselves to go with it.

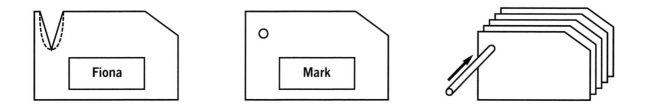

The girls cut a slot in the card as shown. The boys do no cutting at all.

When all the cards are put together (notice the cut off corner – so you know which way up they go!) it is possible to sort the boys from the girls by pushing a dowel through the holes. All the boys' cards will remain on the dowel and all of the girls' will drop off into your hand.

Ourselves

By adding extra holes it is possible to sort for different information. For example, the class might start with the question: *Do all boys with fair hair like salt and vinegar crisps?* They can then construct a card to 'discover' the answer. It will look much like this.

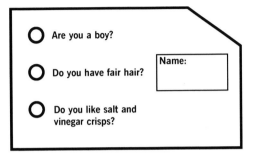

If the answers to the questions are 'yes' then the hole stays in, if 'no' then it becomes a slot.

When all the cards are collected a dowel pushed through the top hole will select all the boys. (The girls' cards can be laid aside for now.) The boys' cards are then taken out and a dowel pushed through the second hole to select those with fair hair and then finally the dowel pushed through the bottom hole will sift out those who like salt and vinegar crisps.

This is how digital computers work. Information is made up of 'noughts' and 'ones', rather like the 'has' or 'has not' sorting above. This is a binary process.

A 'Free Text' Database

A 'free text' database allows users to type in information about things or make collections of their own pictures. These databases can be searched for Keywords. For example, you might write about different animals on each card. The database can then be searched for keywords such as mammal, water-living etc.

Cardfile

The data is relatively unstructured so can be used by very young children. For example, they might make named drawings of themselves. These can be physically sorted into groups of cards: eg. boys and girls. On the other hand, the database can be searched for keywords such as the children's names. Activities using actual cards provide a valuable introduction to electronic software, often called Card Files, which do the same task.

What uses electricity (Key Stage 1)

Collecting information about electrical appliances is both a superb early activity (pages 13–24) and one to use 'free text' databases.

The children brainstorm, with the teacher, all those things that they use, or that they know are used, in their homes and schools that are powered by electricity. The children prepare a card database by cutting items from mail order catalogues and sticking them on cards. These cards can then be sorted physically or can provide the information and inspiration for a computer based activity.

Once the children have used the actual cards, the teacher can set up the computer card file database ready for the children to input information either on their own or with support. The cardfile will allow for the information to be simply entered without format (no fields) so that the children will be able to write exactly what they want. Some cardfiles allow pictures to be imported as well as text. Keywords in the text such as battery, mains, kitchen, school can then be searched.

Observing similarities and differences in rocks and minerals (Key Stage 2)

The 'free text' databases should continue to be used throughout the primary school. For example, it can be used as part of a project on rocks and soils.

The children could use a variety of rock and mineral samples to brainstorm words that they might use in descriptions of the samples. This will help them write notes about the samples, that should include the keywords that will be used for sorting later.

The teacher then uses an electronic card file database and shows the class how to set up the cards ready to input information. As the cards allow for information to be entered without format (no fields), the children will be able to write what they want, but should be encouraged to use the keywords discussed in the first part of the session. Once each person or group has had the opportunity to add to the class database information which they feel is relevant, keywords in the text such as soft, igneous, gritty etc. can be searched to find information about all of the samples that have that particular characteristic.

Flat Files or Single File Databases

One of the earliest types of database young children can be introduced to is the Flat File or Single File database. It can be introduced early in Key Stage 1 and subsequently used in a variety of contexts throughout the primary school.

This type of database stores information in records which have a common format, being divided into a number of pre-determined fields. Before data can be entered, the database must be 'set up' to receive the information.

Setting up a flat file database

Setting up a specific database is described below to show the order in which things are done and to clarify terminology. This example uses a pre-prepared flat file which can be used by teachers. There are many like this available. The software also enables new files and fields to be set up.

The decision to use a flat file database usually begins because there is a question to answer that needs the collection of some information e.g. *Do you think that the children who come to school by car take longer than those who walk?*

This could be answered by collecting information about the way children come to school and how long it takes.

This pre-prepared FILE is called 'My Journey to School'.

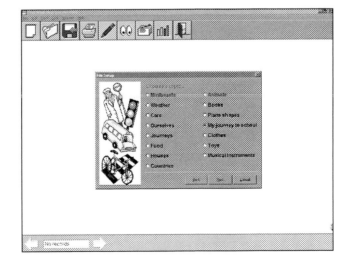

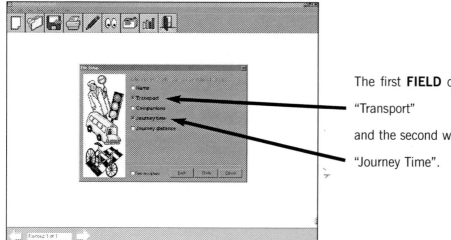

The first **FIELD** of the file will be "Transport"

and the second will be "Journey Time".

The data file will be set up with **KEYWORD** fields so that the children can enter their data quickly from multiple choices which are mutually exclusive.

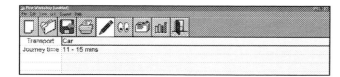

A completed **RECORD** of a journey will appear like the example, left.

The information stored in the File can then be used to answer the original question. It is then first searched for the children who made journeys by car (see right).

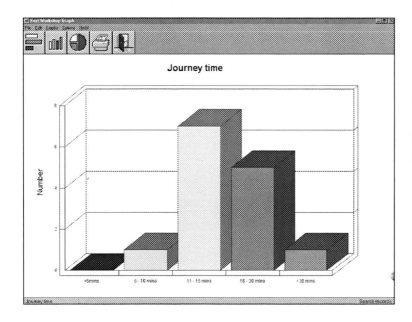

Then the data can be viewed graphically for information about the time of the journeys made by car.

Further graphical information can be obtained by graphing journey times for those children who walked.

These two pieces of information can then be discussed to provide insight into the answer to the question.

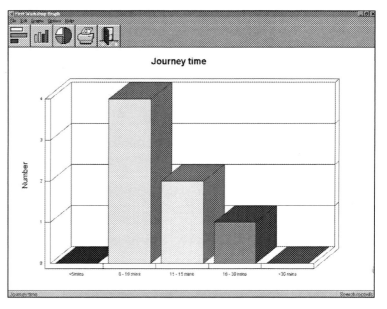

Minibeasts (Key Stage 1)

Minibeast topics are particularly suitable for using Flat Files. The following account describes how a Year 2 class used a prepared flat field database to answer questions about animals in the school grounds.

While the actual activity took place in the school grounds, it required preliminary classroom work to set it up. Initially the children were asked to talk to each other about small creatures they already knew about. This enabled the teacher to produce a list of common animals based on the class knowledge. The teacher also discussed which were likely to be found in the school and the grounds. She then encouraged the children to think about what features the animals had that could form the fields of the flat file database that was going to be used. This pre-excursion stage helped to ensure the children collected all the information they needed.

There are many databases suitable for this task and some are pre-prepared with the fields already in place. These have 'wizards' which allow for quick choice of fields. Others come entirely blank.

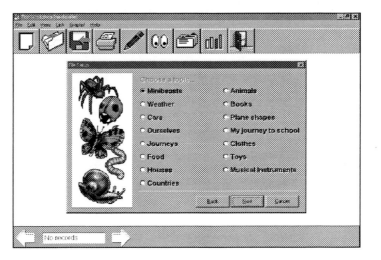

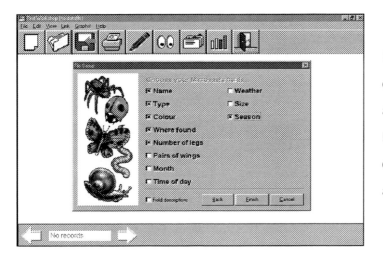

In this example the fields of name, type, colour, where found, number of legs and season have been chosen. The latter was chosen so that the survey could be done at other times of the year and the differences compared.

A 'data capture sheet' with this information on it was prepared and given to each child when they went out into the school grounds. They filled in as much of their data capture sheets as possible. The rest was done with reference to secondary sources on the return to the classroom. Specimens were NOT taken.

Animal name	
Type	
Colour	
Where found	
Number of legs	
Season	

Back in the classroom, the teacher opened the database file and the children (with support as necessary) entered their collected information.

When all of the information had been collected and the gaps filled in, the file was used to answer questions such as:

Did we find all of the worms in the grass?

Do all the creatures with lots of legs live under stones?

On a very practical note it is ALWAYS worth making back-up copies of files prepared by the children, just in case of hard or software accidents!

Properties of Materials (Key Stage 2)

A project on Materials can allow the development and practice of children's ICT skills in using flat file databases in a different science topic. In this particular Year 3 class the main science aim was to help children appreciate that everyday use of materials is related to their properties.

This was a long term activity which lasted over a whole term. A number of activities and experiments were performed with the database being used to store and review the results. There are many database packages suitable for this project. The teacher chose a database that could do progressive searching as well as one that could accept alphanumeric and numeric information. The database also allowed changes to the file after it had been set up and it was able to display graphical information in a variety of ways.

These children were building on work already done in Key Stage 1 where they had been introduced to flat file databases. The children were aware of the nature of a flat file database and had an idea of its structure and its potential for storing a range of information.

The children started the topic by carrying out a survey of materials (wood, glass, metal, rubber, plastic, wool, cotton, ceramics) around the school that had been used for different purposes. They used this experience to think about how to describe different properties. As the teacher was confident using this particular database, she built it up in front of the children and allowed them to make decisions about the necessary fields using their preliminary brainstorm session about the properties of materials.

The children were told that the file structure of the database could be changed as the project developed to take into account the results of their experiments and any other extra information that needed to be added.

Tests were carried out to compare hardness, strength and conductivity that enabled the children to plan and carry out different investigations. The results were recorded on the prepared database. As the term proceeded, additional tests were done that the children had not anticipated, such as on absorbency and stretchiness. Consequently, new fields and new 'cards' for additional objects were added.

The consolidation of all the unit's work included interrogating the database to look for common properties of things used for the same purpose and to find materials that would satisfy a new need.

Branching Databases

Branching databases, sometimes called binary trees, work by the users supplying 'yes' or 'no' answers to a series of questions.

The usual way of building such a database is to select a number of items, say a set of 'living things' and proceed to write questions which divide the items up based on the 'yes' or 'no' answers to carefully written questions. The most general questions are asked first and the more specific ones later. For example, if the database was to be prepared about 'All Living Things' then a sensible first question would be – 'Is it an animal?' This would immediately sort the plants from the animals and allow for the next questions to focus on plants only or animals only. This process eventually identifies each individual item in the database. This is a particularly important type of database for scientists as most biological classifications use this strategy.

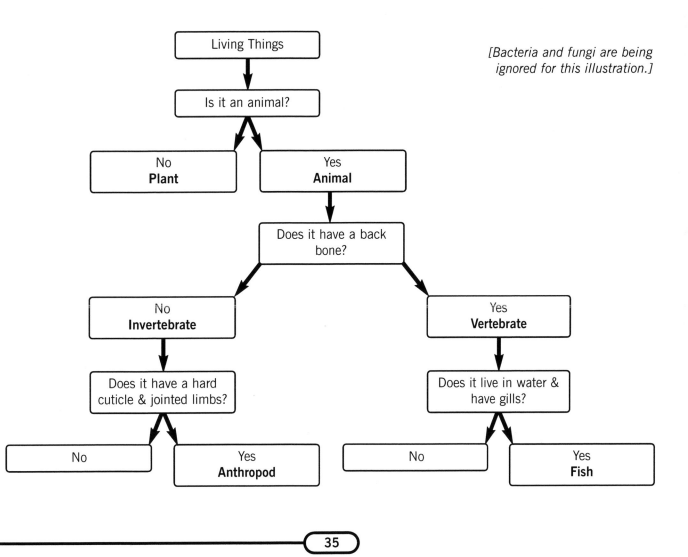

[Bacteria and fungi are being ignored for this illustration.]

Sorting toys practically: Key Stage 1

It is very important to get young children to build simple branching databases themselves. This will help them understand how they work. The first step is to use a few very familiar items and divide them into sets on a large sheet of paper. One Year 1 teacher wanted her class to look at a set of moving toys carefully as part of a topic on *Pushes* and *Pulls*. Over the previous week or so, children had already sorted the toys in many different ways: number of wheels, material, colour etc.

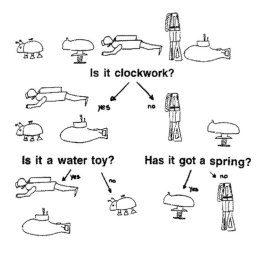

On this occasion, the children were shown five toys and asked to think of one general question that divided the set into two. This avoids the children asking *'Is it a whisk?'* or *'Is it a submarine?'* They suggested *'Is it clockwork?'* This was written down on the paper and the toys divided appropriately into the two groups, Clockwork and Not Clockwork. The children were then asked to focus on one subset and asked to think of a new question to divide this group into two further subsets. This time they suggested *'Has it got a spring?'* They then repeated the process for the remaining set of three toys.

This type of practical sorting activity was done many times under the guidance of the teacher using different toys and then later using different objects relating to other topics, until the task and process was very familiar.

Sounds produced by musical instruments: Key Stage 1

Later on in the year, the class were introduced to using an electronic branching database during their topic on *Sounds and Hearing*.

The teacher introduced the session by playing a variety of instruments: guitar, flute, violin, recorder, keyboard, drum, xylophone etc. She asked the children to listen carefully and see if they could tell what was making the sound and how.

The teacher then used a prepared set of picture cards and reminded the children about the branching databases they had done before. The pictures were attached to a white board right at the top. They brainstormed possible questions to group the items and decided on *Do you produce the sound by blowing it?*

They then built up the branching database on the board. The teacher encouraged the children to think of ways the instruments produced the sounds, although not exclusively.

Having done the activity manually the teacher introduced the electronic version of the branching database and explained that they would use it in exactly the same way. The teacher entered the information into the database while the children observed.

After this initial introduction, the small groups of children were given the opportunity to work with the database they had made together. Later they created a new database for five different instruments using their own questions. Some children were able to add new instruments that they discovered using the CD ROM 'Microsoft Musical Instruments' which is a rich source of new and unusual instruments.

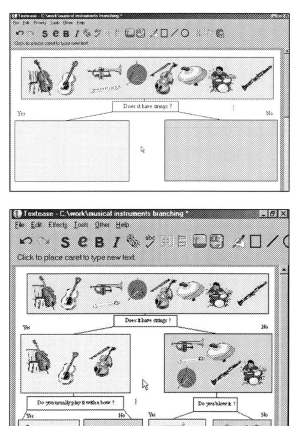

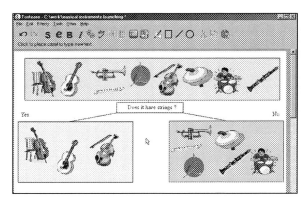

Creating a key for identifying animals or plants: Key Stage 2

Electronic branching databases are particularly appropriate when studying different habitats. The children should have met such databases in Key Stage 1, but may need reminding of the process. One teacher used a prepared set of picture cards and reminded the children how to identify the individual plants and animals by asking specific questions about them, starting from the most general questions first. They then made a paper-based and electronic branching database.

Once the process and the software had been revised, the class walked around the school grounds and jotted down the names of the living things that they saw. Groups made their own branching database using these familiar items. Subsequently, they tried more challenging examples using less familiar animals or plants where they had to focus on minor differences (see over).

Plants

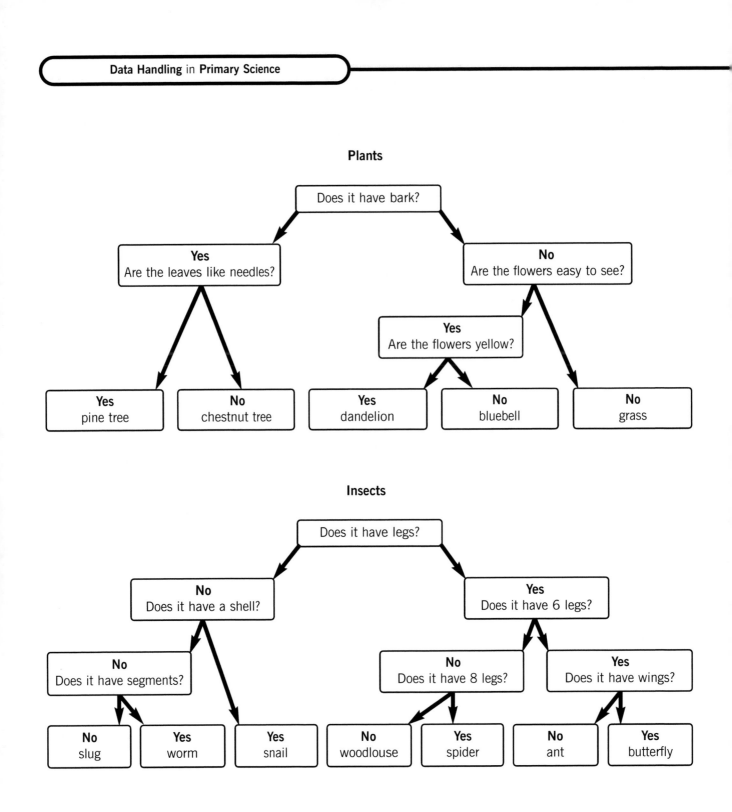

Insects

All these activities involved the children examining similarities and differences of animals and plants. They also provided an excellent foundation to understanding and using biological identification keys, as well as enhancing the children's ICT skills.

Spreadsheets

A spreadsheet is like a flat file database in many ways. Data is stored under similar field headings but spreadsheets can be manipulated in many different ways and are excellent at handling numerical data. They are arranged in boxes, known as cells, and any information – numbers, words, formulae etc. can be entered into an 'active' cell. The cells can be selected and the information in them displayed graphically.

Many software packages have spreadsheets that are suitable for very young children. The ideal type for the primary school is one that has different levels of complexity so that young children can be introduced to the basic processes. Once these have been mastered, higher levels can be introduced progressively.

Spreadsheets should be introduced when the other types of databases are familiar and the children know when to use them. The same process already described with the earlier databases should be used when spreadsheets are introduced. The teacher needs to demonstrate their use in a relevant context and explain why and how it is used.

Materials for Fastening Footwear: Key Stage 1

One Year 2 teacher decided to introduce spreadsheets to her class as part of a project on *Grouping* and *Changing Materials*. This activity was carried out at the beginning of the unit as a way of reminding the children about the names of common materials and how their properties influenced their use. As the children were fairly familiar with the science content, they were able to concentrate on the new ICT skills: namely how to enter information into a spreadsheet and how to review it.

▶ **Session 1: Demonstrating entering, graphing and changing information**

The teacher started the session by asking *'I wonder what is keeping your footwear on your feet today?'* She asked the children how they could find out the answer. After some discussion, the class decided that they needed to collect information about types of fastenings on their shoes. The teacher suggested that this data might be best displayed in a graphical format.

She said that they would use a spreadsheet as this was like flat files they had met before, but these databases meant that the information could be handled quickly and easily.

A simple spreadsheet was used. The teacher demonstrated its use with the keyboard on her knee and monitor by her side. The children sat around the monitor so they could see what was happening. The teacher set up the fields as shown in the first picture.

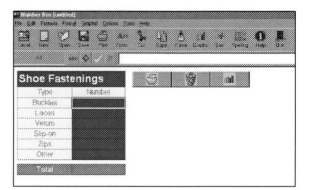

Once the spreadsheet was ready, the data was collected by the children showing hands. They also did a tally chart on the board to help the children make the links between the physical and paper records. The data was then entered into the electronic spreadsheet.

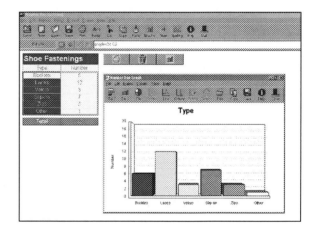

As the items were added to the spreadsheet, the teacher pointed out that the total was automatically calculated as the items were entered. They checked that this was correct by adding up the tallies on the board. It was a very visual way of showing one of the advantages of a spreadsheet. When all the items had been included, the class made a final check to see that the total at the bottom of the column was the same as the number of children present at the time the data was collected.

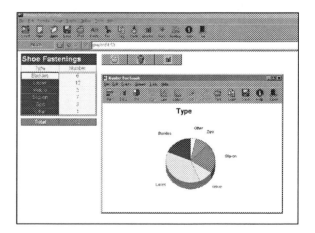

The information was then graphically presented as a block graph and a pie chart. The children could see that they could quickly get a graphical record using the software.

When visitors came into the class, their data was entered on the spreadsheet. The children were fascinated to see the graph change automatically. They enjoyed changing the data to see what would happen.

▶ **Session 2: Collecting data over time**

The teacher wanted to show the children that another advantage of an electronic spreadsheet was that it could handle large amounts of information over time. Consequently, next day the teacher asked *'I wonder why so many of you are wearing lace up shoes today? Is it because they are your 'school' shoes? Or is it because they are your favourites? I wonder if it is like this every day?'* She reminded them of the previous day's work and demonstrated entering a new set of data for the day. This time she asked for help from individuals in the class. They did this for each day of the week. At the end of the week, they discussed the patterns shown by the graphical records.

Practice in other topics

The use of a spreadsheet was subsequently used throughout the year during topics on:

- Different physical characteristics of people, other animals and plants as part of work on *Variation*;
- Foods the children ate as part of a healthy diet project; and
- Medicines used by children in the school as part of the same *Health & Growth* topic.

By the end of the year, the children were able to work in small groups relatively independently of the teacher.

Recording pulse rate with exercise: Key Stage 2

It is important to plan that children will revise and improve their expertise in using different databases throughout the primary school. The planning also needs to take account of

- ICT experience using databases;
- Science topic that needs to be covered; and
- Children's mathematical understanding of graphical representation.

By Year 5, children should be learning to use line graphs appropriately. Therefore, it was decided to include the use of a spreadsheet during a unit on *Keeping Healthy* that would enable a line graph to be used appropriately. These particular children had had experience using simple spreadsheets. They had also been introduced to the use and analysis of line graphs (page 54).

▶ **Session 1: Averaging resting pulse rates**

The class had talked about the relationship between heart beat and pulse rate. They learnt to measure resting pulse rate. The children were then asked *Does everyone have the same pulse rate?* There was a lot of discussion as they noticed that there was variation between people and even the same individual did not always have the same rate. The latter appeared to vary with movement. Consequently they also decided to find out *How does pulse rate vary with exercise? What were the highest and lowest pulse rates?*

Comparing resting pulse rate

The children agreed that they needed a strategy for dealing with individual variations. This led to them creating a record card in which 5 measurements would be taken and averaged (see below).

Activity	Times	Pulse at Rest
• Measure your pulse rate for 30 seconds. • Wait for 30 seconds. • Then measure your pulse for 30 seconds. • Repeat this until you have 5 readings.	Start to 30 seconds	
	1 minute to 1 minute 30 seconds	
	2 minute to 2 minute 30 seconds	
	3 minute to 3 minute 30 seconds	
	4 minute to 4 minute 30 seconds	
	5 minute to 5 minute 30 seconds	
	Average	
	Maximum	
	Minimum	

There was a lot of discussion about calculating the averages which was rather time consuming. Each child's average was compared and a block graph was drawn on the whiteboard.

▶ **Session 2: Using a spreadsheet to compare pulse rates of different levels of exercise**

The teacher suggested that the data could be entered into a spreadsheet which could be set up to make the necessary calculations, as well as create graphs quickly, so that they could focus on analysing and discussing the patterns of results. The teacher demonstrated setting up a data capture sheet. Working in pairs, the class collected the data during a PE lesson (see table, top of next page).

Record card for PE Lesson

Activity	Times	Rest	Walking	Skipping
• Measure your pulse rate for 30 seconds. • Wait for 30 seconds. • Then measure your pulse for 30 seconds. • Repeat this until you have 5 readings. Do this after: • Resting • Walking for 2 minutes • Skipping for 2 minutes	Start to 30 seconds			
	1 minute to 1 minute 30 seconds			
	2 minute to 2 minute 30 seconds			
	3 minute to 3 minute 30 seconds			
	4 minute to 4 minute 30 seconds			
	5 minute to 5 minute 30 seconds			

Back in the classroom the children were shown how to set up the spreadsheet to calculate the average, maximums and minimums. One child's data was entered into the spreadsheet as a demonstration (see right). This data was viewed graphically for interpretation. Later groups entered their data to create their own graphs for comment.

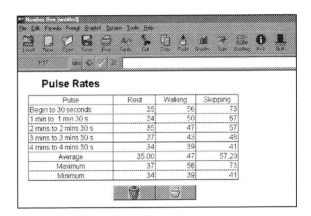

A new spreadsheet was also created to collect all the information from the class. The whole experience had enabled the children to build up a fairly complicated spreadsheet in a way that helped them see how spreadsheets were created. They were also able to talk about the advantages and disadvantages of their use and when they were most appropriate.

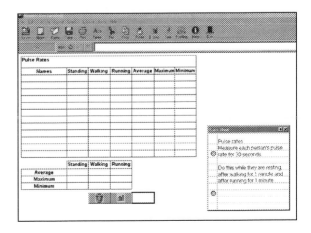

Using **Generic Software Packages** in Data Handling

Generic software, other than databases, can support work in this area. These packages are:

- Word processors
- Graphics packages
- Presentation tools
- Multi-media authoring packages
- Desk top publishers

Word processors allow the storage and revision of text and images. They are simple to use and can be accessed quickly. The data in them can be easily amended. For example, the children coming into the class each morning and typing in their names is an example of collection of data about who is in school on a particular day. This data can then be used for a variety of 'in-class' purposes.

Graphics packages allow the storage of images. For example, Key Stage 1 children drawing a picture of the weather on a graphics package and then saving it so that the images can be reviewed and re-ordered would be using a graphics package as a database.

Presentation packages such as MS PowerPoint allow for the input of text and images and these can be easily arranged and then displayed. Sound can also be added. It is important to remember that data is not just text and numbers but can be sound, still images, moving images as well as animation.

Multi-media authoring packages allow for many different kinds of information to be combined together to make multi-sensory data with modern digital cameras being a key tool to capturing and displaying 'real' information. The WWW and CD ROMs are manifestations of this idea.

Desk top publishing packages provide quick and easy ways of making Venn or Carroll diagrams into which text or graphics can be part of a sorting process.

Developing
Graphical Representation

Introduction

Having decided how to develop a progression in

i)   developing children's independence in using electronic databases; and

ii)   when to introduce different types of database,

a similar progressive introduction of different graphical representation needs to be considered. These must relate to the requirements of the numeracy strategy.

Types of graphical representation

1. Carroll and Venn diagrams
2. Pictograms
3. Block graphs
4. Pie charts
5. Line graphs

Stages to independence

As with the introduction of types of database, there should be a progression from where the teacher models the activities to children's independant and appropriate use of electronic and graphical representation.

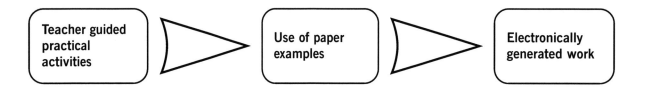

A purpose for graphical representation

It is important to have a purpose for learning about graphs. It is not a separate topic. Without a context for drawing graphs, the children are unlikely to choose the correct type of graph and will struggle to analyse the results in a meaningful way. Line graphs, for example, are often misused because children do not understand that they are only used to represent change.

Graphs are just another method of communicating and clarifying ideas, in the same way as writing is. So in the same way as we need to know when different styles of writing are suitable, we need to help children choose the correct type of graph. There are 'grammar rules' i.e. conventions of graphs and we must be clear about our ideas so as not to mislead the reader. Science topics give many opportunities for developing graphical skills.

The value of electronic graphical generation

Throughout all Key Stages the emphasis is on children generating and collecting their own data. In these situations children 'own' the data and have a feel for how it was obtained. While it is appropriate that the children learn to create these graphs on paper to understand how they are generated, once this has been achieved data from investigations can be quickly and accurately inserted into a computer database so that the focus can be on discussing and analysing the results. Different types and styles of graphs can also be generated in seconds so that the choice of type and graph design is easy to discuss.

Children also need to be presented with new examples. Scientists and non-scientists must be able to make sense of other people's data as well as their own. Prepared electronically produced graphs are clear and can be added to and changed during discussion. All children can be presented with the same data without having to struggle with preparing the graph before interpreting it. This data can be prepared by the teacher or come from existing ICT packages. ICT also enables graphical information to be collected from and shared with others around the world.

Venn and Carroll Diagrams

As with the example given on pages 15–18 where the teacher helped the children sort and record body characteristics, teachers should initially help children to sort actual items before showing them how to represent their sets in Venn diagrams on paper and electronically.

As the children's sorting skills develop they will be able to sort for more than one characteristic, so that more complicated Venn diagrams and Carroll diagrams can be introduced. Teachers need to take care that the number and type of sets are manageable for the children, as well as enabling them to progressively develop their sorting skills.

Two discrete categories Correct use of science language needs to start in the Foundation years. Initially the children should sort real items into two clearly defined categories that focus on learning one word, such as floating and not floating. Once the first concept is established the opposite can be introduced i.e. sinking.

Two or more categories As the children's sorting skills develop, two or more categories can be introduced such as sorting for different colours.

Overlapping sets The problem of items that belong to more than one group can then be introduced such as comparing round and not-round fruit with or without stones.

Less familiar properties Once children understand the sorting process, they should sort for more unfamiliar science concepts such as material (e.g. wood, glass and metal), electrical conduction, energy type etc.

Recording on paper and electronically If items are only sorted physically, it is difficult to remember and compare the results later. Initially the children could draw pictures of the groups they make. As their written language develops they can also write down the names of the items.

However young children's drawing and writing skills are slow to develop. This is where ICT can come into its own. The teacher can provide drawings or names of the items for sorting on the computer which can be 'moved' into appropriate sets. This, of course, should initially be done with the teacher modelling the activity, then working with groups.

A Venn Diagram:

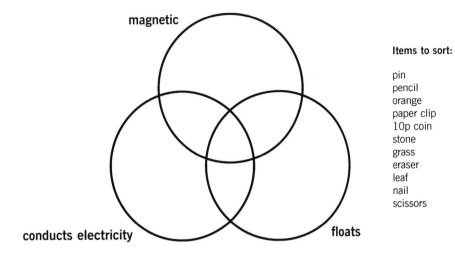

Items to sort:

pin
pencil
orange
paper clip
10p coin
stone
grass
eraser
leaf
nail
scissors

A Carroll Diagram:

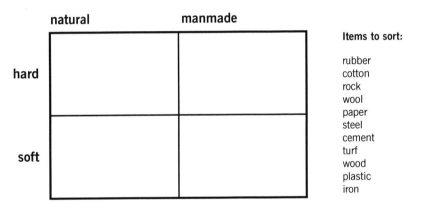

Items to sort:

rubber
cotton
rock
wool
paper
steel
cement
turf
wood
plastic
iron

As the children become more experienced and independent, they can search and collect appropriate drawings for themselves.

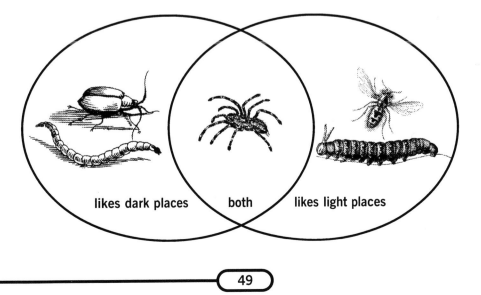

Pictograms

Another way of recording the groups is to ask the children to draw each item on a squared piece of paper which is then used to build up a pictogram. As the children add their pictures to the correct column or line, they will be able to see how a bar chart is created. This is an excellent way of helping the children to make a link between the real item and more abstract representation. (If squares are used, it does not matter which way round the drawing is made. It will still fit correctly into the graph.)

Animals with legs

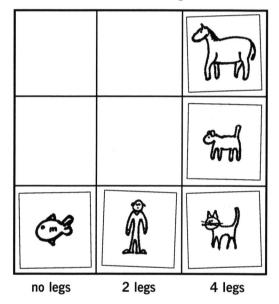

no legs   2 legs   4 legs

Children can be encouraged to discuss the importance of making clear graphs and avoiding misleading readers, either deliberately or by mistake. For example, if the pictures used are not the same size, a false impression can be created as in the pictogram below, where it looks as if the children own more cats than mice.

Our pets

Bar Charts and Histograms

Introducing bar charts

A way of making the link between real items and bar charts is to use different coloured cubes for each category as done by the teacher collecting information about the eye colours in the class (page 16).

Another teacher wanted to collect information about rainfall. Initially the children collected the daily rainfall and put it in a narrow measuring flask. When these were all used, the teacher asked the children what they could do. One child suggested using cubes the same height as the water level. This worked well for several days until they needed the cubes for something else. They then used paper to match the water height. Once the teacher was sure the children still understood that this bar chart showed the rainfall, she demonstrated how they could record the data on a computer which enabled them to add data at different times in the year as well as to print off personal graphs to take home.

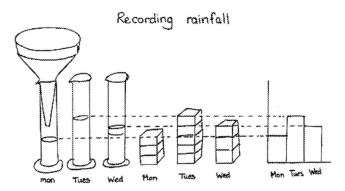

Recording rainfall

Using increasingly complex electronic bar charts

Not only do teachers need to think about whether the children will be able to relate the graph to a real context, they also need to think about the number of items they intend to present to the children and whether the children are ready to cope with the measurements involved.

Generally bar charts that record sets that are described by 'words' or 'keywords' such as hair colour or birthdays are the easiest for children to understand and produce. In these cases there is only one 'field' on an electronic package which will automatically use numbers for the second.

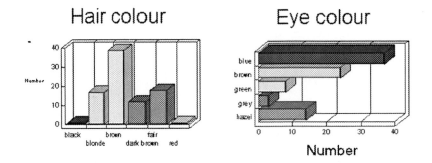

If you want to specify the measurement units, two fields are needed such as name and height, or name and age.

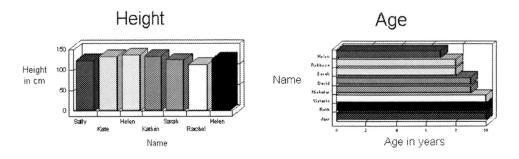

Children should be able to produce the former before creating graphs with numerical values (whole numbers, decimal and money) on both axes.

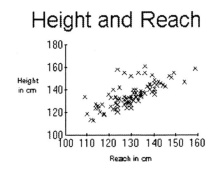

Designing the chart

To help the children realise that a graph should help the reader to make sense of its message, it is helpful to ask the children to consider:

- horizontal or vertical bars; and
- size of scale.

It is fairly obvious that a graph showing height would be better shown by vertical bars, while speed animals run is better as a horizontal bar. Growth of roots is better as vertical bars under a horizontal axis. However, others are not so clear. What would be best for hand span or leaf size? One of the advantages of an electronic version, is that the design can be changed easily once the data has been electronically recorded.

It is also possible to experiment with the scale size with the aim of choosing an honest representation. The two graphs below show the same information. The first appears to show a very heavy rainfall with big daily differences. While accurate it gives a false impression.

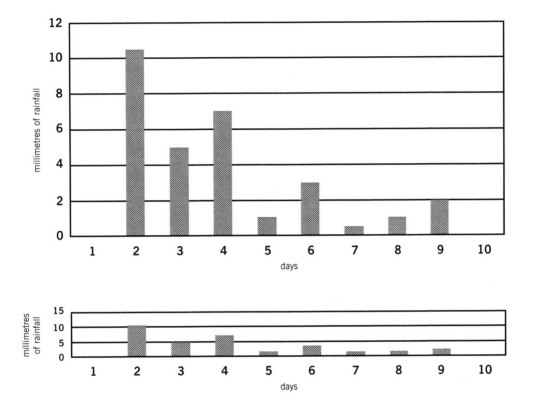

Pie Charts

Pie charts are very difficult to draw by hand but are easily generated electronically. Unlike most other cases, it is easier to introduce the pie chart electronically before a paper version. This type of graph can only be used for graphing one field so could also be used to draw a graph of 'words' or 'keywords' fields such as hair colour or birthdays.

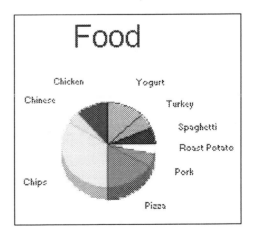

Line Graphs

While line graphs are fairly easily drawn by hand and on computer, they are often incorrectly used. Even although line graphs are usually introduced to children in Key Stage 2, it is just as important to help them make the link between the real phenomena and how the graph is designed.

Considering change

Telling and drawing stories of change can help children to interpret the different gradients of line graphs. One teacher introduced line graphs by telling a simple story of filling the bath with water. (This work is based on an idea from a BBC computer programme called Eureka which may still be in some schools.)

▶ **Stage 1: Introducing gradients and points of change**

The teacher drew two axis: time on the horizontal and depth of water on the vertical. As she told the story, she drew the appropriate line on the graph.

a) The plug was put in and taps turned on.
b) As the water flowed into the bath steadily, a sloping line was graphed.
c) Once the tap was turned off, a horizontal line was drawn because the water depth didn't change.
d) After the plug was taken out and water drained away, the line needed to be sloping.
e) Once all the water had gone, the line needed to be horizontal to show that the depth no longer changed.

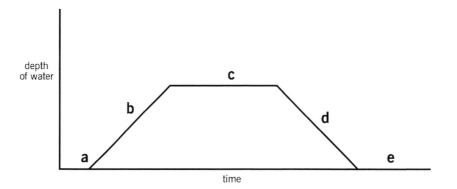

▸ Stage 2: Elaborating the basic story and graph

The teacher repeated the activity, but added elements to the story:

a) The plug was put in and one tap was turned on.

b) As the water flowed into the bath steadily, a sloping line was produced.

c) The other tap was turned on.

 (The children discussed what would happen to the line. They agreed it would be steeper.)

d) The tap was turned off and a horizontal line drawn as before.

e) A little boy got in.

 (Again the class discussed how this would be shown. They decided the line would go up vertically as the height of the water had suddenly gone up.)

f) The boy lay in the bath with the water level steady (horizontal line).

g) The boy got out.

 (The class were quick to say the line would suddenly go down.)

h) The plug was taken out and water drained away so they agreed the line would need to be sloping.

i) Once all the water had gone, the line needed to be horizontal to show no change in water depth.

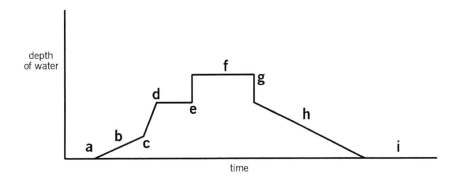

The teacher asked the children to look at different parts of the graph. They noted:

- A horizontal line occurred when there was no change.
- The points where the angle changed was where something different happened.
- A sloping line going up showed more of an increase of something.
- A sloping line going down showed a reduction of something.
- A shallow slope represented a slow increase or decrease.
- A steep slope represented a rapid increase or decrease.

These features were talked about many times in subsequent sessions before all the children appreciated them.

▸ Stage 3: Paired and group activity

The children were asked to think of their own 'bath' story and draw a line graph. Some children were very imaginative and included people jumping in and out of the bath, adding ducks and taking the plug out while still in the bath. Pairs then exchanged graphs (without a story) and tried to produce a new story to match the line they had been given.

▶ Stage 4: Using a new story context

At the beginning of the next lesson, the teacher said they were going to draw line graph stories about plants.

1. The basic story involved a plant that grew steadily until it reached its full height and then was picked.
2. This was elaborated by growth spurts caused by adding fertiliser; periods of no change when there was no growth because someone forgot to water it; and loss of height when a rabbit ate it.
3. The children then created new stories and lines which were shared with their partners as before.

▶ Stage 5. Using a line graph in an investigation

The children planted different plants during the following few weeks in different locations: in the playground, in the classroom and in a dark cupboard. The children kept measurements of the growth and drew the line graphs by hand as well as using a computer.

▶ Stage 6. New investigation contexts

During the rest of the year several other investigations were included, that could use line graphs, including finding out which mugs kept tea hot over time. The latter enabled the teacher to talk to the children about how temperature sensors could collect the data and record it immediately on to a computer screen. Having done the activity practically, they then repeated the investigation using sensors.

This strategy enabled the children to both understand what the computer was recording as well as being enabled to interpret the final line graphs. The class also collected information about changing light patterns in the classroom using sensors, so they could even talk about patterns at night when they were not there.

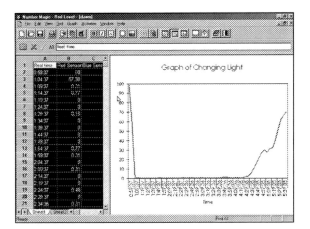

- Remember a line graph is a 'story' about change.
- If a line is drawn between two measured points, the line in-between represents something that happened.

It is very easy to draw beautiful looking graphs on a computer which mean nothing. It is important that children understand what they are doing and can explain what the graph shows.

Appendices

Monitoring Children's Development in ICT

Quick Check Sheet for Data Handling at KS1 and KS2

Key Stage 1 children should be able to:

Manually sort with real things looking at properties, ordering and classification.	
Enter information (text, pictures) into simple collection sheets, looking at the entries and commenting on them.	
Save their work.	
Retrieve their work in a very simple way.	

Towards the end of KS1 and into KS2 children should be able to:

Collect 3 or 4 pieces of information and enter them into a record of a simple database that has been created for their use.	
Use this database to find, display and print records.	
Look at the file and make observations about it.	
Represent some of the data graphically.	
Answer questions about their file and the graphical data.	

Key Stage 2 children should be able to:

Access a file and add information into it.	
Change the information in a file and check the accuracy of what they find there.	
Use simple search facilities and find information from the file.	
Carry out more complex searches.	

At the end of Key Stage 2 children should be able to:

Decide on a simple survey to undertake.	
Design a data capture sheet to collect the information they need.	
Create (with support) their own appropriate database.	
Enter in relevant information.	
Use the file created to answer specific questions.	
Save, retrieve, print and display their work as appropriate.	

ICT Capability Skills for using **Electronic Databases**

Alongside the skills for handling information, ICT capability skills also need to be advanced. The following table gives an indication of those skills involved in data handling that should be considered as the projects and tasks are devised. It is expected that by the end of Key Stage 2 all children will have met all of the skills detailed and will be competent in a good number of them.

ICT CAPABILITY   **DATA HANDLING – DATABASES**

Year R	Year 1	Year 2	Year 3	Year 4	Year 5	Year 6	Skills
							Load software
							Load/Open file
							View records
							Edit records
							Sort records
							Search records – simple
							complex
							Add records
							Check records
							Delete records
							Devise data collection sheet
							Collect data
							Enter data in pre built database
							Save data
							Print data
							Access charts/graphs
							Interpret – bar charts
							pie charts
							histograms
							scattergraphs
							line graphs

ICT CAPABILITY   **DATA HANDLING – SPREAD SHEETS**

Year R	Year 1	Year 2	Year 3	Year 4	Year 5	Year 6	Skills
							Load software
							Open file
							Enter data
							- use cursor key
							- understand cell reference
							- enter text in a cell
							- enter a number in a cell
							- enter a formula in a cell
							- select a range of cells
							Edit Data
							- move around sheet
							- change number in a cell
							- add a range of numbers
							- change column widths
							- delete contents of cell
							- call up a chart
							Statistics/formulae – sum
							difference
							highest
							lowest
							range
							average
							Save data
							Save charts

Jargon Buster

Alphanumeric – a mixture of numbers and letters.

BECTa – British Educational Communications and Technology agency, formerly NCET.

Branching – often refers to a database formed by asking 'yes' 'no' questions.

Cardfile – a program which lets you store information in 'free' form on electronic cards. Allows you to do a key-word search.

Cells – the boxes on a spreadsheet where you put information.

Chart – a graphical representation.

Database 1 – a program which allows you to enter data in a variety of forms.

Database 2 – a collection of information about one specific thing.

Data Capture Sheet – a paper sheet on which the survey of information collected is placed prior to input into the computer database.

Dialog box – a box from which you make a choice e.g. save and load boxes.

Field – the part of a file where a piece of information is stored.

Fieldnames – a title given to each piece of information in a record.

Fieldtypes – the types of information that can be placed in a field.

File – a collection of records. It usually has a name and it is what you save.

Flat file – a file which contains information in a number of fields.

Formulae – you can add these into the boxes of a spreadsheet to do calculations for you.

Icon – a picture on a computer program which does something when you click on it.

Icon Bar – a bar with a whole lot of icons on it.

Keyword – a common word that will be found in free text or can be used in a field. Using keywords in fields cuts down on typing and spelling mistakes (blond, blonde) when entering data in a record.

Line Graph – a graphical representation of changing data.

List – some databases allow you to look at the records as individual cards or in a list form.

Menu buttons – the picture buttons that appear at the top of the windows.

NCET – National Council for Educational Technology now called BECTa.

Numeric – numbers only.

Operator – +, -, X or /

Pictogram – a chart made up of pictures instead of blocks or lines.

Pie Chart – a graphical representation of information that looks like a pie. It represents frequency of 1 field only.

Productivity Package – a generic piece of software such as a word processor, database, graphics package, spreadsheet or presentation package.

Range – a set of cells in a spreadsheet.

Record – a collection of fields.

Scattergraph – allows you to look for the correlation between two numeric fields.

Search – a way of looking for certain information in a file or a record.

Spreadsheet – a program which can handle data in a variety of forms. It is especially good at numbers and can be used to do calculations on the data collected.

Sort – allows you to put the records in order usually numerical or alphabetical.

Survey – the collection of information.

Video Buttons – these are the buttons often found on the bottom icon bar of a database which allow you to move around the information quickly.

Resources

The examples given below are not intended to be all-inclusive lists. They are intended to give a start to teachers and students beginning to develop ICT within their science work.

Useful websites

Some of these sites are for children with information at child level and some are for teachers to raise subject knowledge and to support ideas. Most will have some content for both purposes. Teachers will need to visit these sites and spend time deciding whether the information / simulation / activity displayed enhances their teaching and the children's learning.

Virtual Teachers Centre – http://www.vtc.ngfl.gov.uk/vtc/curriculum

chem4kids – http://www.chem4kids.com

e4S have some animations – http://www.e4s.org.uk

QUEST – http://www.nhm.ac.uk/education/quest2/english/index.html

Science Web has some interactive stuff – http://www.scienceweb.org.uk/index.htm

Volcano World – http://volcano.und.nodak.edu/vw.html

Science Museum – http://www.nmsi.ac.uk

Roger Frost's site – http://www.rogerfrost.com

Books

IT in Primary Science by Roger Frost (ISBN 0 9520257 3 6)

This is a really useful book that gives a lot of help to assist planning. It is packed full of curriculum ideas and references.

Software for Science Teaching by Roger Frost (ISBN 0 9520257 5 2)

This is a complete list of software, including CDs. It has been compiled by Roger Frost, one of the foremost writers and lecturers in this area of ICT.

Getting Started with Information Handling BECTa (ISBN 1 85379 293 4)

This is an BECTa pack containing lots of support and ideas to get you started! The pack contains 10 practical activity cards and disk files for the activities.

Computer Based Learning by J. Underwood David Fulton Publishers (ISBN 1 85346 298 5)

IT Across the Curriculum Cassell (ISBN 0 304 33290 9)

Information Handling Special Microscope MAPE Journal

Software Houses

Anglia Multimedia	Rouen House, Rouen Road, Norwich, NR1 1RB Telephone: 01603 760 000 http://www.anglia.co.uk/education
BlackCat Educational Software	Granada Learning Ltd., Granada Television, Quay Street, Manchester, M60 9EA Telephone: 0161 827 2927 http://www.blackcatsoftware.com
Edu Tech Systems	The Woodstock Centre, Freepost, Leicester, LE4 2ZY Telephone: 0116 2350355
Granada Learning	Granada Television, Quay Street, Manchester, M60 9EA Telephone: 0161 827 2927 http://www.granada-learning.co.uk
Inclusive Technology	Saddleworth Business Centre, Delph, Oldham, OL3 5DF Telephone: 01457 819790 http://www.inclusive.co.uk
Kudlian Soft	8a Nunhold Business Centre, Dark Lane, Hatton, Warwickshire, CV35 8XB Telephone: 01926 842 544
Logotron	124 Cambridge Science Park, Milton Road, Cambridge CB4 4ZS Telephone: 01223 425558
Microsoft Ltd	Microsoft Place, Winnersh, Wokingham, Berks, RG41 5TP Telephone: 01734 270759
RM	New Mill House, 183 Milton Park, Abingdon, Oxon, OX14 4SE Telephone: 01235 823338
Semerc	Granada Television, Quay Street, Manchester, M60 9EA Telephone: 0161 827 2927 http://www.granada-learning.co.uk
Sherston Software	Angel House, Sherstone, Malmesbury, Wilts, SN16 OLH Telephone: 01666 840433 http://www.sherston.com
Softease	Market Place, Ashbourne, Derbyshire, DE6 1ES Telephone: 01335 343 421
SPA	PO Box 59, Tewkesbury, GL20 6AB Telephone: 01684 81700
Storm	Coachman's Quarters, Digby Road, Sherborne, Dorset, DT9 3NN Telephone: 01935 817699
TAG	25 Pelham Road, Gravesend, Kent DA11 OBR Telephone: 01474 357 350 http://www.tagdev.co.uk
Topologika Software	Islington Wharfe, Penryn, Cornwall, TR10 8AT Telephone: 01326 377771

Note: References and sites were correct at the time of writing.

ToolKits

Many software companies put together generic toolkits. These are sets of software which integrate together to provide users with the ability to communicate in text, graphics, charts and tables.

It is worth contacting BlackCat Educational Software, Edu Tech, Granada Learning, RM, and Softease, amongst others, for details of these integrated packages.

Some Software Distributors

Schools Direct CD ROM   The Green, Ravensthorpe, Northampton, NN6 8EP
Telephone: 01604 770099

REM   Great Western House, Langport, Somerset TA10 9YU
Telephone: 01458 253636

AVP   School Hill Centre, Chepstow, Mon, NP6 5PH
Telephone: 01291 625 439

Some Science and ICT Organisations

ASE, Association for Science Education, College Lane, Hatfield. AL10 9AA.

Telephone: 01707 267411; Fax: 01707 266532

www.ase.org.uk

BECTA, Milburn Hill Road, Science Park, Coventry CV4 7JJ.

Telephone: 01203 416994; Fax: 01203 411418

www.becta.org.uk/index.cfm

RSC, Burlington House, Piccadilly, London, W1J 0BA.

Telephone: 020 7437 8656

www.rsc.org/lap/educatio/rsedhome.htm

References

Department for Education and Science (2000) *A Scheme of Work for Key Stages 1 and 2: Information Technology* London: Qualifcations and Curriculum Authority

Department for Education and Science (2000) *A Scheme of Work for Key Stages 1 and 2: Science* London: Qualifcations and Curriculum Authority